The Beatles

Wise Publications
London/New York/Paris/Sydney

Exclusive Distributors:
Music Sales Limited
8/9 Frith Street, London W1D 3JB, England.
Music Sales Pty Limited
120 Rothschild Avenue, Rosebery, NSW 2018, Australia.

This book © Copyright 1992 by
Wise Publications
Order No.AM89912
ISBN 0-7119-3087-2

Music engraved by Interactive Sciences Limited, Gloucester
Cover designed by Hutton Staniford
Music arranged by Stephen Duro
Compiled by Peter Evans

Photographs courtesy of:
Retna Limited

Music Sales' complete catalogue lists thousands of titles and is free from your local music shop,
or direct from Music Sales Limited. Please send a cheque/postal order for £1.50 for postage to:
Music Sales Limited, Newmarket Road, Bury St. Edmunds, Suffolk IP33 3YB.

All My Loving

Words & Music by John Lennon & Paul McCartney

And I Love Her

Words & Music by John Lennon & Paul McCartney

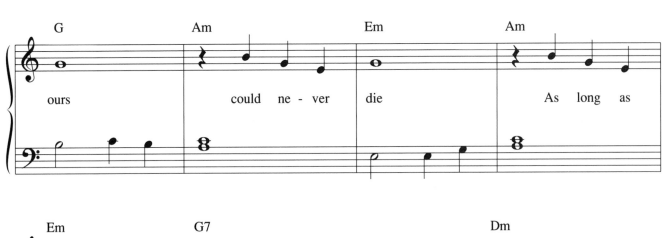

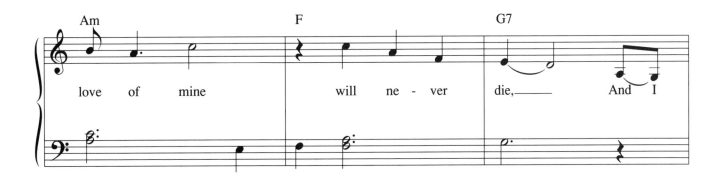

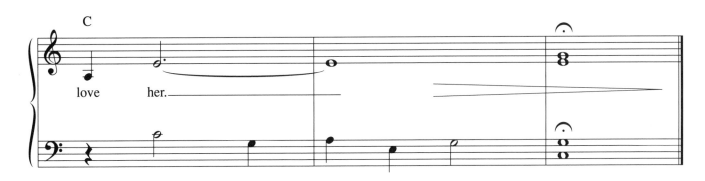

Eleanor Rigby

Words & Music by John Lennon & Paul McCartney

Moderately with a beat

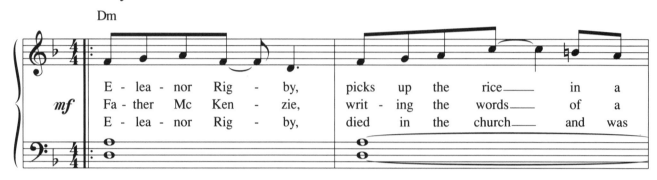

E - lea - nor Rig - by, picks up the rice in a
Fa - ther Mc Ken - zie, writ - ing the words of a
E - lea - nor Rig - by, died in the church and was

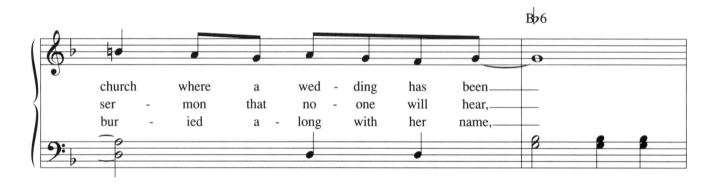

church where a wed - ding has been
ser - mon that no - one will hear,
bur - ied a - long with her name,

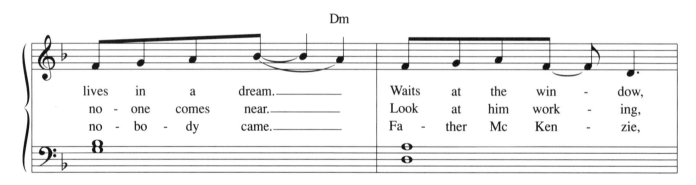

lives in a dream. Waits at the win - dow,
no - one comes near. Look at him work - ing,
no - bo - dy came. Fa - ther Mc Ken - zie,

wear - ing the face that she keeps in a jar by the door,
darn - ing the socks in the night when there's no - bo - dy there,
wip - ing the dirt from his hands as he walks from the grave,

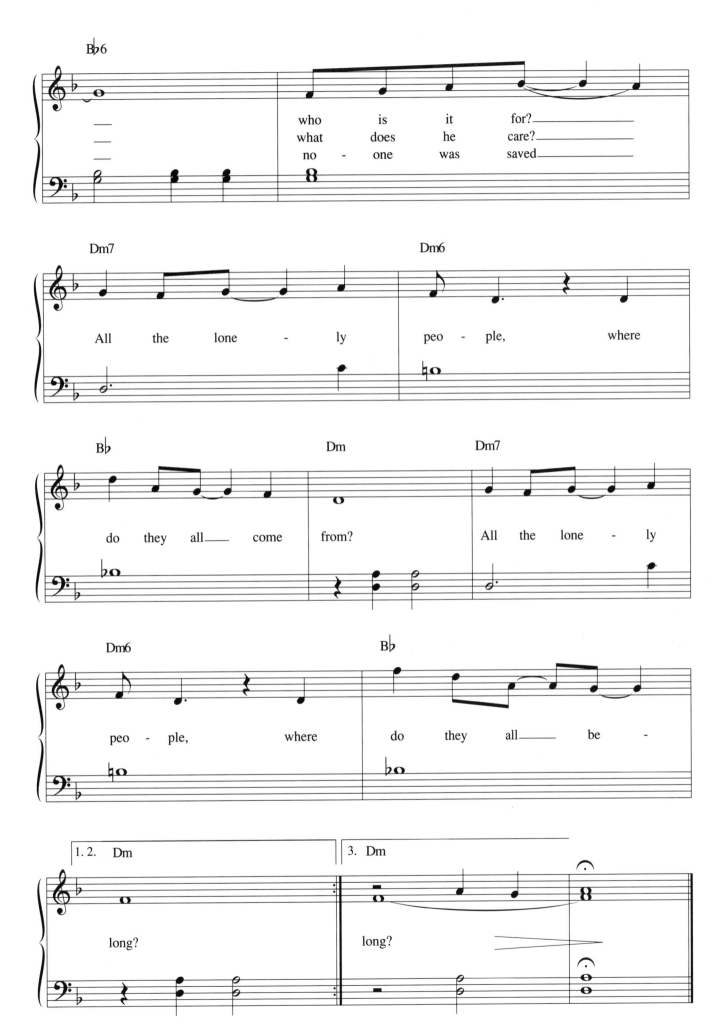

Get Back

Words & Music by John Lennon & Paul McCartney

Hey Jude

Words & Music by John Lennon & Paul McCartney

Lady Madonna

Words & Music by John Lennon & Paul McCartney

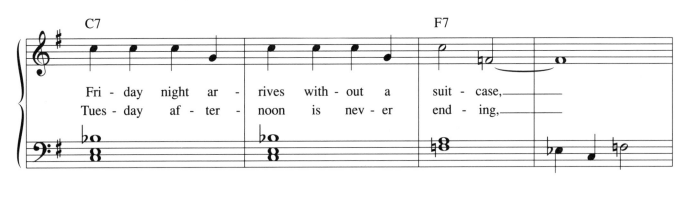

Fri - day night ar - rives with - out a suit - case,___
Tues - day af - ter - noon is nev - er end - ing,___

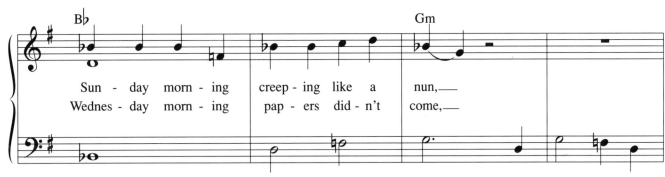

Sun - day morn - ing creep - ing like a nun,___
Wednes - day morn - ing pap - ers did - n't come,___

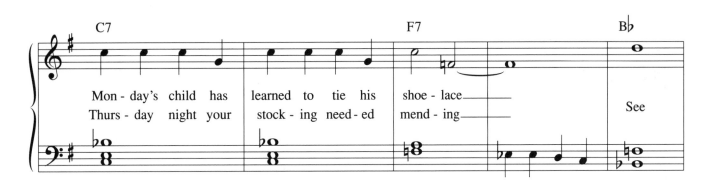

Mon - day's child has learned to tie his shoe - lace___
Thurs - day night your stock - ing need - ed mend - ing___ See

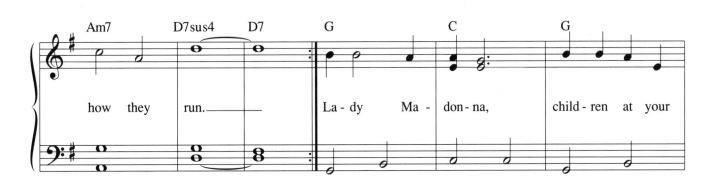

how they run.___ La - dy Ma - don - na, child - ren at your

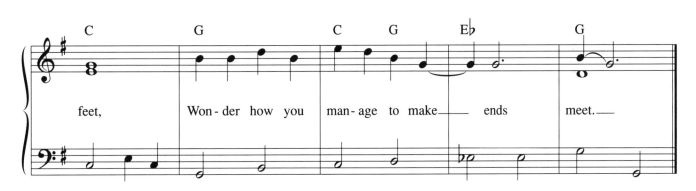

feet, Won - der how you man - age to make___ ends meet.___

15

Let It Be

Words & Music by John Lennon & Paul McCartney

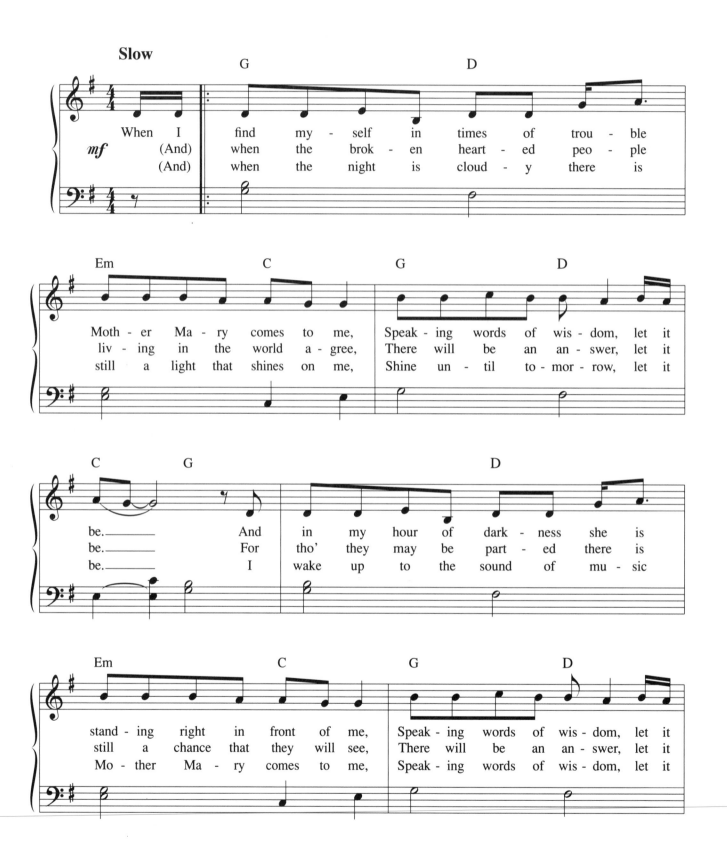

Michelle

Words & Music by John Lennon & Paul McCartney

Moderately

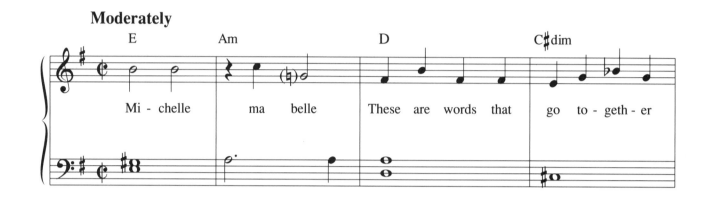

Mi - chelle ma belle These are words that go to - geth - er

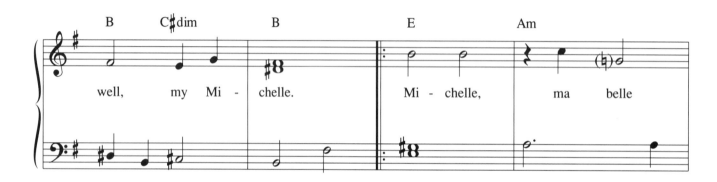

well, my Mi - chelle. Mi - chelle, ma belle

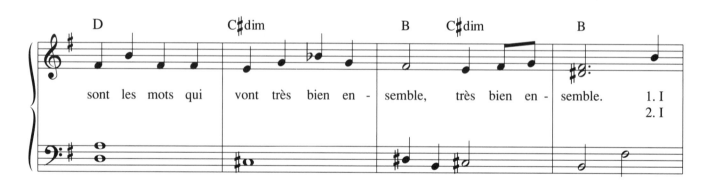

sont les mots qui vont très bien en - semble, très bien en - semble.

1. I
2. I

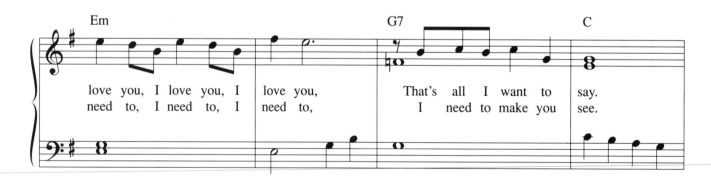

love you, I love you, I love you, That's all I want to say.
need to, I need to, I need to, I need to make you see.

Norwegian Wood

Words & Music by John Lennon & Paul McCartney

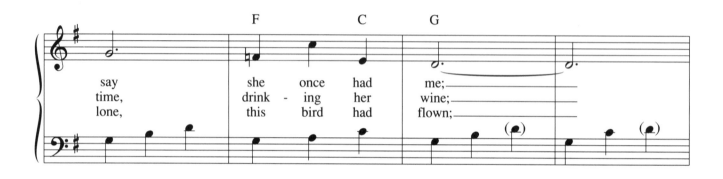

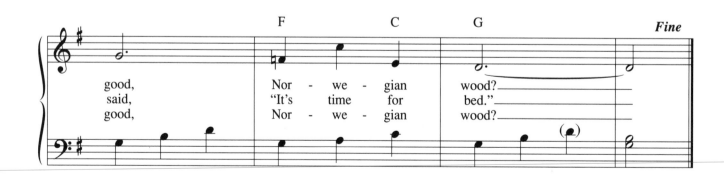

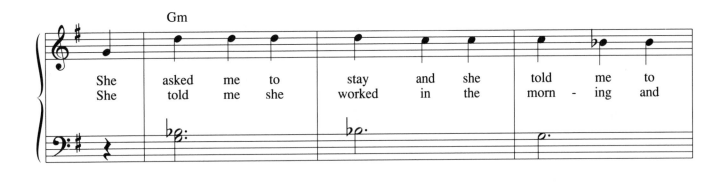

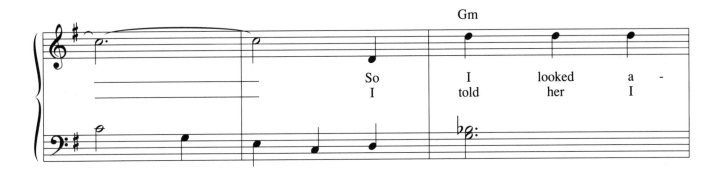

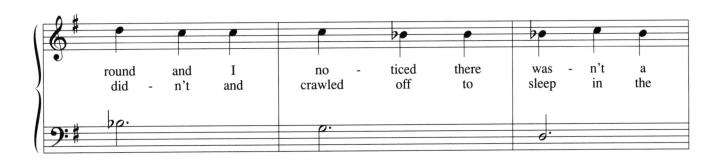

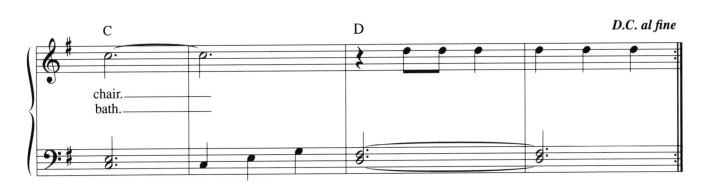

Paperback Writer

Words & Music by John Lennon & Paul McCartney

Ticket To Ride

Words & Music by John Lennon & Paul McCartney

2.
B♭7
I don't know why she's rid - ing so high, she ought to
think right, she ought to do right by me.
C
B♭
Be - fore she gets to say - ing good - bye, she ought to think right, she ought to do right by me.
C
D.𝄋 al Coda 𝄌
3. She
𝄌 CODA
Dm
Cm
F
she's got a tick - et to ride but she don't care.
My ba - by don't care.

With A Little Help From My Friends

Words & Music by John Lennon & Paul McCartney

Moderately bright

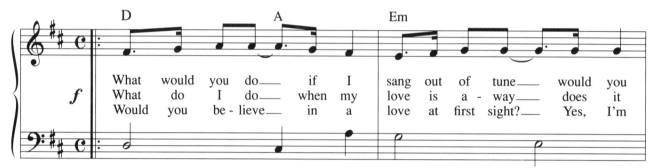

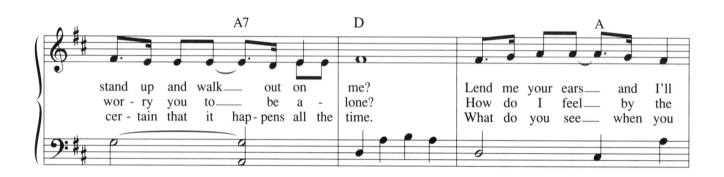

Yellow Submarine

Words & Music by John Lennon & Paul McCartney

Yesterday

Words & Music by John Lennon & Paul McCartney

Slowly

31

A Hard Day's Night

Words & Music by John Lennon & Paul McCartney

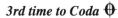

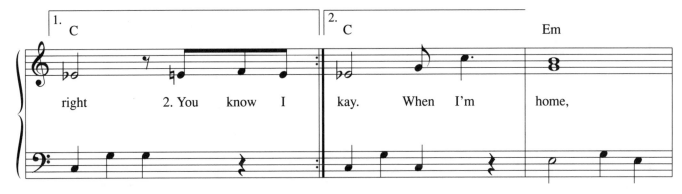

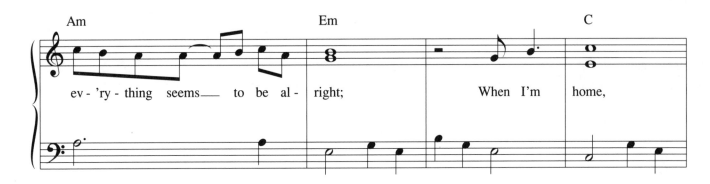

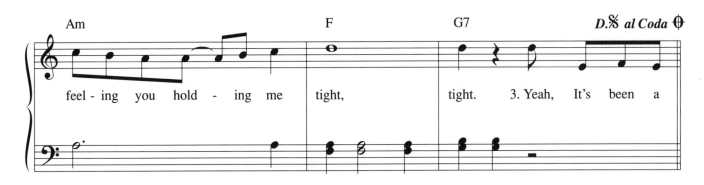

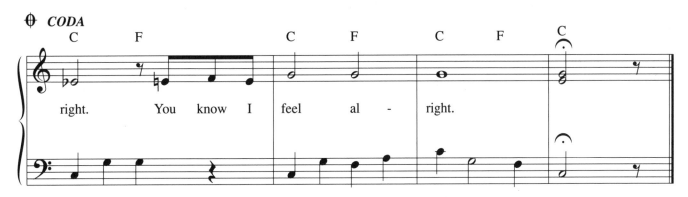

33

When I'm Sixty Four

Words & Music by John Lennon & Paul McCartney

The Fool On The Hill

Words & Music by John Lennon & Paul McCartney

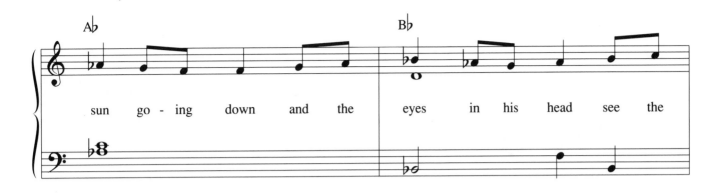

sun   go - ing   down   and   the   eyes   in   his   head   see   the

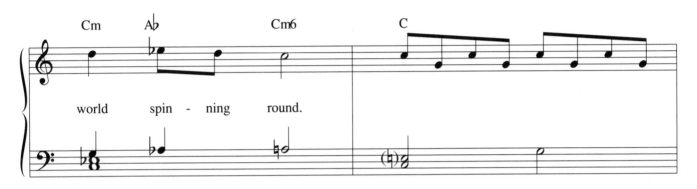

world   spin - ning   round.

2. Well on the way, head in a cloud,
    The man of a thousand voices talking perfectly loud,
    But nobody ever hears him or the sound he appears to make.
    And he never seems to notice,
    But the fool (*etc.*)

3. Day after day alone on a hill,
    The man with the foolish grin is keeping perfectly still,
    And nobody seems to like him, they can tell what he wants to do
    And he never shows his feelings,
    But the fool (*etc.*)

4. Day after day alone on a hill,
    The man with the foolish grin is keeping perfectly still,
    He never listens to them, he knows that they're the fools
    They don't like him.
    But the fool (*etc.*)

If I Fell

Words & Music by John Lennon & Paul McCartney

love me more than her.   If I | hurt my pride like her. 'Cause I

could - n't stand the pain and I would be sad if our new

love was in vain. So I hope you see that I would

love to love you and that she will cry when she learns we are two. 'Cause I

CODA
she learns we are two, if I fell in love with you.___

39

Can't Buy Me Love

Words & Music by John Lennon & Paul McCartney

41

In My Life

Words & Music by John Lennon & Paul McCartney

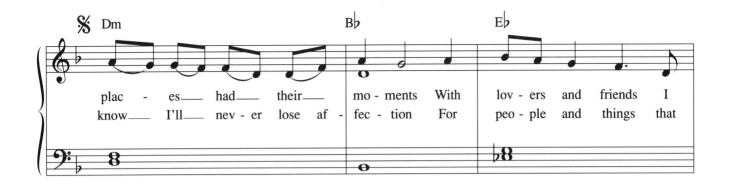

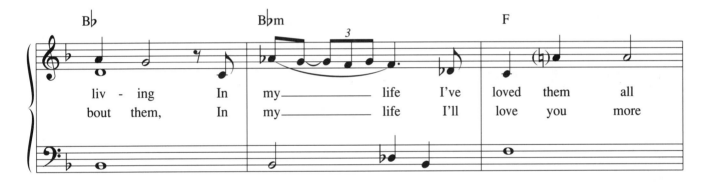

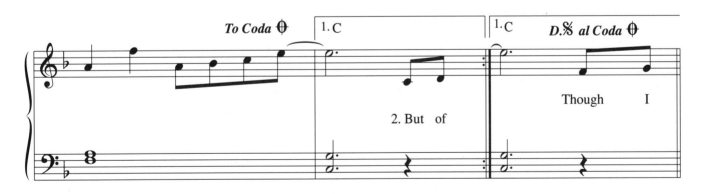

43

I Want To Hold Your Hand

Words & Music by John Lennon & Paul McCartney

2. Oh please, say to me, you'll let me be your man.
And please, say to me, you'll let me hold your hand.
Now let me hold your hand, I wanna hold your hand.

4. Yeh you, got that something, I think you'll understand.
When I, feel that something, I wanna hold your hand.
I wanna hold your hand, I wanna hold your hand.

The Beatles: Music Books In Print

The Best Of The Beatles: Book 1
NO18541 £5.95

The Best Of The Beatles: Book 2
NO18558

**The Best Of The Beatles: Book 3
Sgt. Pepper**
NO18566

The Best Of The Beatles : Book 4
NO18608

The Best Of The Beatles: Book 5
NO18616

**Beatles Big Note: Piano/Vocal
Edition**
NO17428

**Beatles Big Note:
Guitar Edition**
NO17402

**A Collection Of Beatles Oldies:
Piano Vocal Edition**
NO17659

**A Collection Of Beatles Oldies:
Guitar Edition**
NO18004

**The Beatles Complete: Piano/
Vocal/Easy Organ Edition**
NO17162

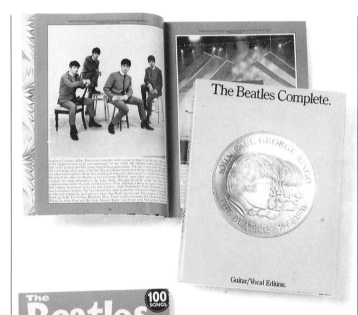

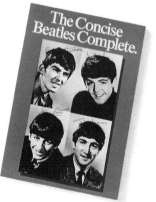

The Beatles Complete (Revised)
Re-engraved, revised edition of 'The
Beatles Complete'. For piano/organ/
vocal, complete with lyrics and
guitar chord symbols. Includes
every song composed and recorded
by the group. 203 songs, plus
24-page appreciation by Ray
Connolly, lavishly illustrated with
rare photographs.
Piano/Organ/Vocal Edition
NO18160
Guitar/Vocal Edition
NO18145

The Beatles Bumper Songbook
Full piano/vocal arrangements of 100
songs made famous by the Fab Four.
Includes 'All You Need Is Love',
'Yellow Submarine', 'Lucy In The Sky
With Diamonds' and 'Hey Jude', all
complete with lyrics. 256 pages in all.
NO17998

The Concise Beatles Complete
NO18244

**The Beatles Complete: Chord
Organ Edition**
NO17667

**The Beatles Complete: Guitar
Edition**
NO17303

The Beatles: A Hard Day's Night
NO17576

Beatles For Sale
NO17584

The Beatles: Help
NO17139

The Beatles: Highlights
NO18525

The Beatles: Let It Be
NO17055

The Beatles: Love Songs
NO17915

**The Beatles: Magical Mystery
Tour**
NO17600

The Beatles 1962-1966
NO17931

The Beatles 1967-70
NO17949

The Beatles: Revolver
NO17568

The Beatles Rock Score

Twelve numbers scored for groups.
Perfect note-for-note transcriptions
from the recordings for vocal and
each instrument, in standard notation
and guitar tablature. Includes drum
line and lyrics.
NO18442

Rubber Soul
NO17592

The Singles Collection 1962-1970
NO17741

The 6 Chord Songbook
NO18418

The 6 Chord Songbook: Book 2
NO18517

20 Greatest Hits: Piano/Vocal Edition
NO18269

20 Greatest Hits: Easy Guitar
NO18277

White Album
NO17469

The Songs Of George Harrison
AM30990

The Great Songs Of George Harrison
AM37649

The Great Songs Of John Lennon
AM61854

KEYBOARD/PIANO SONGBOOKS

101 Beatles Songs For Buskers
Includes all their favourite songs
in melody line arrangements,
complete with lyrics and guitar
chord boxes.
Piano/Organ Edition.
NO18392

Beatles Best for Keyboard
HD10029

The Complete Keyboard Player: The Beatles
NO18509

The Complete Piano Player Beatles
NO18806

Creative Keyboard Series: The Beatles
AM71911

Home Organist Library: Volume 9 Beatles Songs
NO18186

The Beatles. 100 Hits For All Keyboards
Special lay-flat, spiral-bound
collection of favourite Beatles songs
arranged for all keyboards – piano,
electronic piano, organ and portable
keyboards. With full lyrics.
NO18590

It's Easy To Play Beatles
NO17907

It's Easy To Play Beatles 2
NO90342

SFX-3: Beatles Hits
AM33093

SFX-16: Beatles Hits 2
AM39660

GUITAR

Beatles Guitar: Tablature
NO18798

The Complete Guitar Player: The Beatles
NO18491

The Beatles For Classical Guitar
NO17444

The Beatles For Classical Guitar: Book 2
NO17782

Fingerpicking Beatles
AM30941

WIND INSTRUMENTS

Beatles For Recorder
NO18434

Greatest Hits For Harmonica
NO18673

Beatles: Themes And Variations: Clarinet
NO17873

Beatles: Themes And Variations: Flute
NO17865

Beatles: Themes And Variations: Trumpet
NO17881

Lennon & McCartney For Clarinet
NO17725

Lennon & McCartney For Clarinet
NO18764

Lennon & McCartney For Flute
NO18756

Lennon & McCartney For Saxophone
NO18772

Lennon & McCartney For Trumpet
NO17733

Lennon & McCartney For Trumpet
NO18780

Lennon & McCartney 60 Greatest For Trumpet
NO18715

GERMAN EDITIONS

Beatles Für Die Blockflöte
MG13582

Die Beatles Für Klassische Gitarre: Band 1
MG13202

OMNIBUS PRESS

The Beatles Apart
PRP10083

The Beatles Book
OP43439

The Complete Beatles Lyrics
OP42027

With The Beatles: The Historic Photographs Of Dezo Hoffmann
OP41961

Beatles: In Their Own Words
OP40419

Paul McCartney: In His Own Words
OP40047

Available from all good Music Shops.

In case of difficulty, please contact:
Music Sales Limited
Newmarket Road, Bury St. Edmunds, Suffolk IP33 3YB, England.
Telephone: 0284 702600. Fax: 0284 768301. Telex: 817845.

The Beatles

Enya

Phil Collins

Van Morrison

Bob Dylan

Sting

Paul Simon

Tracy Chapman

Bringing you the words

Eric Clapton

Pink Floyd

New Kids On The Block

All the latest in rock and pop. Plus the brightest and best in West End show scores. Music books for every instrument under the sun. And exciting new teach-yourself ideas like "Let's Play Keyboard" - in cassette/book packs, or on video. Available from all good music shops.

Bryan Adams

Tina Turner

Elton John

and

Bee Gees

Whitney Houston

AC/DC

music

Music Sales' complete catalogue lists thousands of titles and is available free from your local music shop, or direct from Music Sales Limited. Please send a cheque or postal order for £1.50 (for postage) to:

Music Sales Limited
Newmarket Road,
Bury St Edmunds,
Suffolk IP33 3YB

Buddy

Five Guys Named Moe

Les Misérables

West Side Story

Phantom Of The Opera

Show Boat

The Rocky Horror Show

Bringing you the world's best music.